Wilf and Wilma had come to play at Biff and Chip's house. It was Wilf's birthday.

"Happy birthday, Wilf," said Biff and Chip.
They gave him a big card.

1

Wilf had a large box.

"This is my birthday present," he said.

Everyone looked inside the box.

"What is it?" asked Chip.

"It looks like a submarine," said Biff.

"It's a kind of submarine," said Wilf.
"It explores the sea bed."

"That's right," said Wilma. "It goes to
the bottom of the sea."

"What a brilliant present!" said Biff.

The submarine looked like a car. It
had big windows and it had headlights.
Wilf put the headlights on.

"It's brilliant," said Chip.

Biff looked at the magic key. Suddenly it began to glow. It was time for a new adventure.

"I wonder where the key will take us," said Wilf.

The magic took the children to the
sea, where there were lots of boats.
Wilma pointed to a yellow submarine.

"Look at that one," she said. "It looks
just like Wilf's submarine!"

The children went to look at the submarine.

"I wish we could look inside," said Chip.

Just then a hatch began to open and a man looked out.

The man peered at them.

"Hello!" he said. "I'm Professor Tangle."

"How do you do," said Wilf.

"My new crew?" said Professor Tangle. "You look a bit young."

"We're not your new crew," shouted
Wilf. "How do you do!"
Professor Tangle didn't hear properly.
He got things muddled up.
"You know what to do?" he said.

"That's good! Get on board," went on
the Professor. "And tell me your names."
"I'm Biff," said Biff, "and this is
Wilma. This is Wilf, and this is Chip."

"No, it's not a ship," said the Professor. "It's a diving machine."

"We know that," said Wilf.

"We've never been in one," said Wilma, "and we're not your new crew!"

"You flew?" said Professor Tangle. "I didn't see an aeroplane. Now shall we go?"
Everyone smiled, and they all climbed into the submarine.

Professor Tangle shut the hatch.

"There's not much room," said Wilma.

"No," said Biff. "I hope it doesn't leak."

"Of course you can speak," said the Professor.

Professor Tangle started the engines.
"It's time to dive," he said.
The submarine went under the water.
"Glub! Glub! Glub!" it went.
Everyone looked out of the window.

They could see fish everywhere.

"It's wonderful," said Chip. "It's amazing to be under the sea."

"You can't see?" said Professor Tangle. "Look out of the window, then."

"Come on, crew!" said Professor Tangle. "Time to do some work. Push that button, Biff. Press that handle, Wilf. Pull that lever, Chip."

"We're not the crew!" yelled Biff.
"Things might go wrong."

"Sing a song?" said Professor Tangle.
"There's no time for that. There's far too
much to do."

The submarine began to dive. It went deeper and deeper.

"Glub! Glub! Glub!" it went.

"Where are we heading?" shouted Chip. "Will we dive deep?"

"No, you can't go to sleep," said
Professor Tangle. "You're the crew! You
have to stay awake! We are going to dive
deep."

"This thing scares me," said Wilma.

The submarine went deeper and
deeper.

"Glub! Glub! Glub!" it went.

Everyone looked out of the window.

"I can see a shark!" said Wilma.

"It *is* getting dark," said the Professor.

The submarine went even deeper.
Professor Tangle was excited. It began to
get dark.

"It's getting very dark," said Biff.
"Put the lights on, Professor."

The Professor pushed the light switch.

"Bother! The lights don't work," he said.

Biff looked out of the window.

"Oh no! Help! Professor Tangle! I can see huge rocks," she called.

"No, I don't need clean socks," said
the Professor. "Now, where's that fuse?"
He began to look for his tool box.

"Look out!" yelled Chip. "We're going
to crash!"

Professor Tangle pushed a button and he pulled a lever. The submarine didn't crash. It just missed the rocks.

"Phew! That was close," said Wilma.

There was a cave ahead of them. The
submarine was heading for it.

"Slow down, Professor," called Wilf.
"We are heading for a cave in the rocks."

"Yes, it was in the box," said the
Professor.
He held up the fuse.
"Professor, slow down!" yelled Wilf.
"We're going into a cave."

"Well, why didn't you say so?" asked
Professor Tangle. "We'd better slow
down."
He pulled a lever and the submarine
slowed down just in time.

The submarine went into the cave.
Professor Tangle put the new fuse in. All
the lights came on. The cave shone and
sparkled. There were diamonds all over
the walls.

"Diamonds! I'm rich!" said the
Professor.

"But you can't get at them," said Biff.

"Oh bother!" said Professor Tangle.
Suddenly the walls of the cave began to
shake.

Rocks and stones fell all around them.

"We must get out," said the Professor. "Full speed ahead."

"Oh no! We aren't going to make it," said Wilma.

The submarine got out just in time.
"Phew! That was close!" said Biff.
"We're sorry you couldn't get the
diamonds, Professor," said Chip.
Just then the key began to glow.

The magic took them back to Biff's room.

"That was a good adventure," said Chip.

"We must go home for tea," said Wilma.

"What's that?" joked Wilf. "You want to go back to sea?"